Craig Saves
the Day

Written by Roderick Hunt
Illustrated by Nick Schon,
based on the original characters
created by Roderick Hunt and Alex Brychta

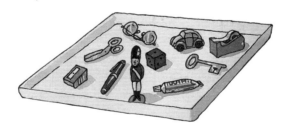

OXFORD
UNIVERSITY PRESS

Say the sound and read the words

ai

Gail

wait

tails

Craig

ay

day

hooray

stay

play

a–e

- ate
- race
- game
- lake

"So this is Haygate Lake,"
said Chip.

Gail was the leader.

"Wait for Craig," she said.

"Let Chip push me," said Craig.

"It's a fun day with games and races," said Gail.

"You stay in the same team
all day," she said.

Wilf, Chip and Craig were in the
red team.

They played a game called 'Tails', but
the green team won.

They played 'Kim's Game'. Craig
was good at it.

"Hooray," yelled Chip.
"We won. The red team won."

It was time to eat.
Wilf had a cake.

He gave it to Gail and they all
ate some.

They had an egg and spoon race.
The green team won.

They had a pea race and Craig
won it.

The last game was a boat race.

Craig won the race.

"Good for Craig," said Chip.

Talk about the story

Why was Chip glad that Craig was in the red team?

Which games was Graig good at?

What games do you like to play?

ai, ay or a-e?

The sound 'ai' can be spelled *ay*, *ai* and *a-e*. Match the right 'ai' spelling to the pictures and complete the word.

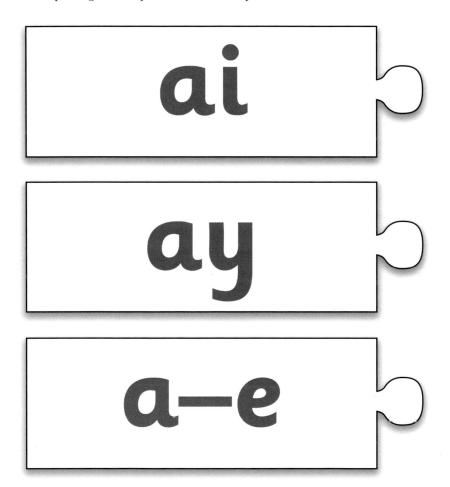

g_m_

r__n

pl__

Cr__g

tr__

g_t_

Picture puzzle

Find as many *ai*,
ay and *a–e* words as
you can in the picture.

ay

a-e

Answers: Craig, Gail, Haygate Lake, cake, plate

Jumbled letters

Make the *ai, ay* and *a–e* words from the story.

ai	w	t

t	l	ai	s

ay	t	s

h	ay	r	oo

a	k	e	l

m	a	g	e